The POETRY BUG

Andy Tooze

illustrated by
Martin Olsson

Matador
9 Priory Business Park,
Wistow Road, Kibworth Beauchamp,
Leicestershire. LE8 0RX
Tel: 0116 279 2299
Email: books@troubador.co.uk
Web: www.troubador.co.uk/matador
Twitter: @matadorbooks

ISBN 978 1784625 450

British Library Cataloguing in Publication Data.
A catalogue record for this book is available from the British Library.

Printed and bound by CPI Group (UK) Ltd, Croydon, CR0 4YY
Typeset in 11pt Aldine401 BT by Troubador Publishing Ltd, Leicester, UK

Matador is an imprint of Troubador Publishing Ltd

MIX
Paper from
responsible sources
FSC® C013604

Dedicated to Emily, Connie and Beth, with love.

ANDY TOOZE

www.thepoetfromthepeaks.co.uk

contents

A Few To Get You Going

For Twenty Words Fans

For Family Fans

For School Fans

For Feelings Fans

For Fitness And Football Fans

For Fans Of Animals And Nature

For Fans Of Maths And Tongue Twisters

For Body Fans

For Final Thoughts Fans

A Few To Get You Going

WHOSE DAY

Monday. The Moon's day.
Whistle a back-to-school tune day.

Tuesday. Tiw's day.
Last weekend's now old news day.

Wednesday. Woden's day.
Middle of the week, hold on day.

Thursday. Thor's day.
God of thunder roars day.

Friday. Freya's day.
Last day before we can play day.

Saturday. Saturn's day.
Weave your own patterns day.

Sunday. The Sun's day.
Another week is done day.

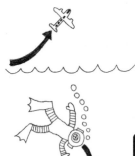

OPPOSITES

New old
Hot cold
In out
Whisper shout
Up down
Smile frown
Kind mean
Dirty clean
Hope fear
Boo cheer
Break mend
Beginning end

cHEAT

Choose a five-letter word, let's use cheat.
Take the C from the front, feel the heat.
When the H has gone too you can eat.

Now the E has been stolen by the cat.
Can you see where it's at?
All this excitement is too much for me.
I'll take away the A and relax
With a nice cup of T.

NORMAL NORM

He's Normal Norm
My garden gnome.
I found him in a skip
So I brought him home.

Norm the Gnome
Doesn't say a lot,
And he's not really bothered
If it's cold or hot.

He's not great at cuddles
Because he's made out of stone.
But I love Normal Norm,
My garden gnome.

MY FAVOURITE WORDS

Slurp, freckles, rhythm,
Intuition, parakeet.
Sparkle, sausages,
Tambourine, sweet.
Sigh, dusty, whisper,
Liquorice, Zanzibar.
Gorgeous, murmuring,
Antelope.
Ta ra!

5

TEN USES FOR A BANANA

Use it as a boomerang. Throw it.
Take it to school, impress your friends. Show it.
Trail it behind you on a piece of string. Tow it.
Bury it in some soil. Grow it.
Make a banana your pal. Know it.

Always say hello to your banana. Greet it.
Rub its skin to warm it up. Heat it.
Take it to a restaurant. Treat it.
Hold its chair while it sits down. Seat it.
Peel it and gobble it up. Eat it!

TOO MUCH

I don't like being greedy
But sometimes I am.
One time I ate a whole packet of biscuits
Fifteen or so,
One after another, just like that.
The first two or three were nice.
I enjoyed them.
After that it became a habit,
A horrible habit.
One more, one more, one more
Until they were all gone.
I felt sick, I felt soiled.
I never ever wanted to see another biscuit,
Let alone eat another biscuit.
I wanted to punish myself
So I went for a run
Over the hills and far away,
Three miles or so.
My stomach really hurt.
It felt like I was carrying a sack of bricks inside me!

That biscuit binge was about ten years ago.
I tell you what.
I've eaten plenty of biscuits since,
But I've never eaten a whole packet, in one go, again!

A-Z IT'S ALL IN THE HEAD

A is for A, like A sausage or A sack.

B is a buzzy thing ready to attack.

C is huge and wet with waves and seaweed slime.

D is "Excuse me, what is dee time?"

E is a name: "E's my best friend."

F is a posh "of": "F course I'm quite round the bend."

G is half a horse: "Would you like to ride my gee-gee?"

H is how old you are: "My H is fifty three."

I is one of those things that enable you to see.

J is a woodland bird flitting from tree to tree.

K is a girl's name spelled KAYE.

L is a horrible hot place, not at all heavenly.

M is a sound you make when you're not sure what to say.

N is a chicken, clucking and pecking all day.

O is a sound you make when you get a surprise.

P is what you want when you're bored but the teacher says: "You're telling lies."

Q is lining up and waiting for stuff.

R is a rustic way of saying yes: "Arr that's enough."

S is a posh "is": "S that my piece of cheese?"

T is a drink made from funny little leaves.

U is you! Not them, me or us.

V is we in certain dialects: "Ve are looking for ze London bus."

W is, I suppose, two lots of u.

X is gone, finished, like chewing gum under a table is an ex-chew.

Y is a question: "Why write a poem when you could play football?"

Z is the head: "Ze head is full of nonsense."

That's all!

For Twenty Words Fans

TWENTY WORDS ABOUT EVOLUTION

Monkey man,
Australopithecus.
Left the trees,
Became like us.
Explored the plain.
Stood upright,
Enjoyed the view.
Is that right?

TWENTY WORDS ABOUT SHARKS

No claws or paws,
Just jaws,
Full of gleaming, razor teeth
With which to drag you underneath.
Glug, glug, glug.

TWENTY WORDS ABOUT BLACK PUDDING

Black pudding,
Ecky thump.
Animal innards in a lump.
Lancashire delicacy.
Brekkie or tea.
Once a year's enough for me.

TWENTY WORDS ABOUT A cARPET

My pet mouse
Doesn't live in my house.
It lives in my car.
Together we travel far.
It's a carpet.

TWENTY WORDS ABOUT
ALL CHARGED UP

Retrieve charger from the bin.
Find the phone, plug it in.
Wait a while.
Eat, sup.
Hallelujah.
All charged up.

TWENTY WORDS
ABOUT JELLYFISH

Quavering, quivering,
Floating, shimmering,
Oscillating, pulsating.
Mysterious, transparent, ancients of the deep.
How many long-lost secrets do they keep?

15

TWENTY WORDS ABOUT cATS

Cats are:
Scatterers [of birds]
Flatterers [of owners]
Chatterers [when they're hungry]
Batterers [of defenceless fledgelings]
Cats are ferocious felines!

For Family Fans

The Daddy

I'm the daddy, I'm the daddy,
I'm your big main man.
I'm the daddy, I'm the daddy,
I'm your number one fan.
I'm the daddy, I'm the daddy,
I'm your tip top guy.
I'm the daddy, I'm the daddy,
You're the apple of my eye.
I'm the daddy, I'm the daddy,
I want you to know,
That I am your daddy,
And I love you so!

17

OUR GRANNY

Our Granny knocks other grannies flat.
Our Granny wears a funny hat.
Our Granny tried to iron our cat.
Our Granny's great.

Our Granny makes strange faces during tea.
Our Granny thinks everything in the shops is free.
Our Granny is the family celebrity.
Our Granny's great.

Our Granny's in a class all of her own.
Our Granny lives in a special home.
Our Granny doesn't like being left alone.
Our Granny's great.

Our Granny's not allowed to drive a car.
Our Granny gets lost if she walks very far.
Our Granny sometimes forgets who we are.
But our Granny's great!

MY BEST SHADOW

Inspiring me, supporting me,
Delighting me, enthralling me,
Always, always, always.
Vivacious and free.
Just how we should be.
Always, always, always.
Your music will always echo
Around the caverns of my soul
For without your love
I would never be whole.
My perfect dream.
My best shadow.
My Beth.

BABY IN A BUGGY

Baby in a buggy,
Buggy ran away.
Baby says: "Goo goo ga ga."
It's all that it can say.

Baby in a buggy,
Going downhill fast.
Many people staring,
As buggy races past.

Baby in a buggy,
Baby likes the ride.
Baby feels quite comfy
Wrapped up safe inside.

Baby in a buggy,
Heading for the sea.
Baby chatters merrily,
"Goo goo ga ga gee."

Baby in a buggy,
Buggy lands on yacht.
Sails away from home
To somewhere where it's hot.

Baby in a buggy,
Goes to many places.
Sees all kinds of people
With many different faces.

Baby in a buggy,
Has a homesick pain.
Baby misses mummy
So sails back home again.

Baby in a buggy,
Meets up with its mum.
She's been waiting for a while,
But she's happy now it's come.

Baby in a buggy,
Back at home at last.
Says: "Goo goo goo goo ga ga."
Which means: "Wow that buggy's fast."

Baby in a buggy,
Safe and snug in bed.
Adventure now is over,
Cuddles favourite ted.

THE INVISIBLE MAN

The invisible man has gone away,
I won't see him again today.
I won't see him again next week.
It's not that he's some sort of freak,
It's just that he's my far-away Dad.
People say it's not so bad
To see him every other Sunday.
But it's a long wait for our fun day.
Sometimes it gets me really mad.
Other times I just feel sad.
The invisible man has gone away,
I won't see him again today.

LiFE AND dEATH

We used to have a hamster called Hammy.
But now he's dead.
He used to sleep inside the piano
On hay he'd carried to make a bed.

I used to have a dad
But now he's dead too.
However, my mum's still enjoying life,
And she's eighty two.

DON'T DISS DANCING DADS

Don't diss dancing dads
Coz that is what I am.
Don't diss dancing dads
Coz I'm that man.

Don't diss dancing dads
For what else should I do?
Should I just stop dancing
Now my younger days are through?

Do you want me just to stay in bed
Or hobble around with a stick?
Crying out in a croaky voice:
"I'm getting old and sick!"

No way. I'm a dancing dad.
I don't intend to hide.
So don't diss dancing dads
I'll shout it far and wide.

Next time the music pounds
And the dudes hit the floor,
I'll be boogying with them
Then crying out for more.

So don't diss dancing dads
Coz that is what I am.
Don't diss dancing dads
Coz I'm that man!

For School Fans

ASSEMBLY

I'm not sure what assemblies are for.
Perhaps it's lots and lots of practice
In sitting on the floor.

FiRE DRiLL

When we all line up in the playground,
Without making a single sound,
I always get wibbly wobbly knees,
And I feel like having a giant sneeze.
I get this urge to scream and shout.
I want to jump and run about.
But I don't.
I just answer, "Yes Miss," to my name.
I wonder if the other children
Always feel the same.

DINNER LADIES

Where do they come from?
Where do they go?
No one on earth will ever know.
They may be from outer space
Or the dark side of the moon.
They may get up early,
But they're never seen until noon.
Just after two they creep stealthily away,
Not to be seen again until the next day.
During the weekend
They may hide underground,
Talking in whispers,
Hardly making a sound.
But come Monday lunchtime
They reappear to our sight,
Keeping their secrets locked away tight.

Where do they come from?
Where do they go?
You can search high or
You can search low
But except for two hours during the week
You'll fail absolutely
To find the evidence you seek.
During school holidays
Who knows where they go?
Perhaps under the sea or
Sledging on snow.
But when term starts again
On the very first day
Their uniforms are spotted
Just before midday.
Then the whispers go round
With a slight shiver of fear:
"They're back. They've returned.
The dinner ladies are here."

GiANT SPiDER

There's a giant spider
On the paper towel container.
It's just sitting and watching and waiting
For poor little Kirsty to dry her hands.
Then:
Leap, crunch, munch, burp.
It'll be all over in less than a minute.
When her mum comes to pick her up
At the end of the day,
There'll be just a coat with no Kirsty in it!

30

READY, STEADY, GO
FRIDAY 3.15 P.M.

Nearly the weekend
Everybody ready.
Excitement is mounting,
Got to keep steady.
Waiting for the bell.
Why is time so slow?
There it is!
It's the weekend.
Here we go!

WET PLAYTIMES

"I'm just going to the staffroom
To grab a cup of tea.
No mucking about any of you,
Or you'll have to answer to me."
The teacher's gone. The classroom's ours.
We've only got five minutes,
But it feels like hours.
We sit on the tables,
And stand on the chairs.

The boys munch sweets
While the girls comb their hair.
The boys play the girls at football
With chairs for the posts,
Cheers for slide tackles,
And whoever scores the most.
The lookout is calling:
"The teacher's on her way."
We now move the quickest we've moved all day.
Chairs back in places,
Sweet papers in the bin,
Combs back in bags,
Jack stops fighting with his twin.
Reading books out, silence in the room.
"Jack, switch on the light.
There's a good lad.
Two house points for everyone,
And tell your mums and dads
You're a credit to the school, yourselves and to me.
It's so great I can trust you
When I go to get my cup of tea!"

DON'T TEASE THE TEACHER

Don't tease the teacher.
She's a fragile creature.
Treat her with care.
Don't jeer and stare.
Bring her in a sweet
For a special treat.
Don't pick your nose
Or tread on her toes.
Pretend you like school
And that you think she's cool.
Be really kind.
Your mum won't mind.
But above all,
Don't tease the teacher.
She's a fragile creature.

TEN cLASS RULES

One: Don't wiggle your bum.
Two: Don't chew.
Three: Don't pester me.
Four: Don't slam the door.
Five: Don't skive.
Six: Don't try any clever tricks.
Seven: Don't forget this classroom is child heaven.
Eight: Don't be late.
Nine: Don't chat in the line.
Ten: Don't forget these rules again.

THE BiRDBOY

Birds have hollow bones.
That's why they can fly.
If I had hollow bones,
I'd follow them across the sky.
Everyone in the playground
Would stand still and stare.
They'd shout:
"Look there's the Birdboy flying in the air."

I'd give flying lessons
To a few of my mates.
They'd say: "Thanks Birdboy.
Your lessons are great."
Then we'd whizz through the air
Flying together.
We'd only go back to school
In really bad weather.

36

The teachers would shout:
"Come down Birdboy, you've had your fun.
Come back into class
And do your sums."
But I'd proudly shout back
At the top of my voice:
"You'd be up here with me
If you had the choice."

But my bones aren't really hollow,
They're solid as can be.
So I can't fly at all,
At least not when anyone can see.
But in my imagination
I'm the Birdboy of the air,
Soaring, gliding and swooping,
In my perfect life without a care.

FIDDLEITIS

It's hard to stop fiddling
When the pencil's just there,
Asking to be picked up.
It's hardly fair
That I can't get hold of it
And roll it around in my hands,
Or dangle it from my nose.
All that is banned.

It's hard to stop fiddling
But so easy to start.
Stopping is without doubt
The trickiest part.
That rubber was just asking
To be flicked in the air.
I just couldn't resist it.
It was only a dare.

38

It's hard to stop fiddling.
And now I'm in trouble.
I've been sent to the office
With my mate, at the double.
We're waiting outside,
A pen is just lying around.
I bet I could balance it on my nose.
My mate has bet me a pound.

It's hard to stop fiddling.
I've lost my bet.
And now the pen is on the floor.
If only I could stop fiddling
But I keep coming back for more.
Those pencils and pens
Keep singing you see:
"Fiddle, oh fiddle, oh fiddle with me!"

PLAYGROUND GOSSIP

They've got a new plan.
I heard it from my Gran.
The teachers have had enough.
They're going to get really tough.
They've bought some brand new gear
Which made even Mrs Jones cheer.
From now on they can
Lasso us with a great thick rope.
[That's especially to help the dinner ladies cope.]
Or
Put us to sleep with a tranquilliser dart
The next time someone lets out a … rude noise.
Or
Trap children who are fighting in a net,
Just like they're catching a runaway pet.
Or
Release us through a secret trap door
Then leave us in a cellar until ten past four.

 40

Do you know the very worst thing of all?
They've bought a robot that's ten feet tall.
If he wants to give you a scare
He can pick you up and hurl you in the air.
Then when you've crashed back to the ground
You hear this terrible cranking sound.
His horrible fingers tickle your toes,
He puts his metallic face against your nose
And says:
"Next time you're feeling naughty just pause,
Or you'll see some more Robot Wars."

41

THE PIRATE

"Shiver me timbers, walk the plank."
Guess who came to school?
Only a pirate all hairy and wild.
We thought he was really cool.

In his deep voice he called me "Jim Lad"
Even though my name's Tom.
In between swigs from his hip flask
He kept on singing this song:

"A pirate I was born,
A pirate I will stay.
I'm only having one day off
To visit a school today."

With his black eye-patch and wooden leg
He was an incredible sight.
He showed us hundreds of golden coins
Which he said he'd won in a fight.

Polly Parrot on his shoulder
Danced as the pirate sang.
But Polly started squawking
When we heard an incredible bang!

"It's me ship calling me 'ome,"
Our pirate friend explained.
Quick as a flash he was off down the road.
Only a parrot feather remained.

But of course we'll keep our memories
Of the day a pirate came to school.
They may be fierce in battle,
But we say: "Pirates rule!"

cHEWiNG GUM oN TEAcHER'S cHAiR

Chewing gum on teacher's chair.
All sticky and covered with hair.
Chewing gum on teacher's chair.
It's making all the children stare.
Chewing gum on teacher's chair.
I only brought it in to share.
Chewing gum on teacher's chair.
Oh no, it's stuck right there.
Chewing gum on teacher's chair.
She's sat on it, watch out, beware!
Chewing gum on teacher's chair.
"Miss, I'm stuck," laughter everywhere.
Chewing gum on teacher's chair.
She's growling, she knows it's there.

 44

Chewing gum on teacher's chair.
Sorry Miss, next time, more care.
Chewing gum on teacher's chair.
She's after me, she's escaped from her lair.
Chewing gum on teacher's chair.
She's a six-legged monster, it's not fair.
Chewing gum on teacher's chair.
No escape anywhere!
Chewing gum on teacher's chair.
Wake up screaming.
What a nightmare!

45

ART

Paint on the walls
Paint on the door
Paint on the taps
Paint on the floor

Paint on my fingers
Paint in my hair
Paint on my jumper
Paint everywhere

Painting disaster.
Too much of a rush.
I only really wanted
A little paint on my brush!

School TRIP

No kicking, no hitting,
No swearing, no spitting.
No making rude signs from the bus.
No chewing, no pouting,
No sulking, no shouting.
No "I need the loo" silly fuss.

No prodding, no jabbing,
No screaming, no stabbing.
No moaning, "I'm feeling sick."
No whistling, no lying,
No crocodile crying.
Remember I know every trick!

No jumping, no dancing,
No singing, no prancing.
No knowing what you lot will do.
No break time, no hope.
How on earth will I cope?
Just me, on this bus, with you!

47

TEN THINGS TEACHERS NEVER SAY

The field's soaking wet, but you can go on it anyway.
Maths test tomorrow, so you can play all day today.
Don't worry about finishing your work. I don't really care.
So what if you never get a turn? I'm not trying to be fair.
Leave your homework for tonight. You all need to get out more.
Why do you come in so quietly? I wish you'd slam the door.
Don't bother tidying up. I love a bit of clutter.
Just don't speak so clearly. I prefer it when you mutter.
If you can't find a tissue for your nose, why not pick it out?
Please don't work so quietly. I love it when you shout!

SPLITTING THE CLASS

Daniel, you go to class one,
Ayesha, you go to two.
Jess, you're off to class three,
Nat, you work in the loo.

Amelia, you work in the kitchen,
Josh, you stay outside.
Naomi, please keep an eye on Josh,
Make sure he doesn't hide.

Gurpreet, up to the roof please,
Jack, you swing from the lights.
Lisa, would you go from class to class please
Sorting out all the fights.

Majid, you work in the office,
Ben, you just go home.
All of you, have a nice afternoon.
I'm staying here on my own!

DISASTER DAY

Sick on the floor,
Sick on the floor.
Poor little Lauren's been sick on the floor.

Now there's more,
More than before.
Poor little Lauren's been sick on the floor.

It's ever so lumpy,
All yellow and bumpy.
Poor little Lauren's been sick on the floor.

It's horribly smelly,
From deep in her belly.
Poor little Lauren's been sick on the floor.

There's some on Jack's hat,
And more on the mat.
Poor little Lauren's been sick on the floor.

It's gone on Jade's dress,
Oh, what a mess.
Poor little Lauren's been sick on the floor.

Lauren is crying,
She's sobbing and sighing.
Poor little Lauren's been sick on the floor.

She's been taken away.
We've been sent out to play.

We heard Miss Brown say:
"It's Disaster Day!"
All because
Poor little Lauren's been sick on the floor!

FoR FeeLings FAns

MATES

Give me a sweet. Shan't!
Come round after school. Can't!
Let's play chase. Won't!
You eat worms and spiders. Don't!
You're in a mood. So!
Tell me what's up. No!
When's your mum's operation? Today.
Do you want to come into lunch with me? Okay.

LiTTLE MiSS iNVISIBLE

I'm Little Miss Invisible when I'm sitting on my chair.
I'm Little Miss Invisible. No one knows that I am there.
I'm Little Miss Invisible when I'm sitting on the floor.
Quite why I'm Miss Invisible, I'm not exactly sure.
The boys are not invisible,
Nor is my loud friend,
Even though her talking drives the teacher round the bend.
She still gets more team points than me,
Just like all those boys,
The ones who have a competition
To see who can make the most noise.
Teachers tell us to be well behaved.
They tell us to be quiet.
So how come children get more attention
When they are causing a riot?
It doesn't seem quite right to me,
It doesn't seem quite fair,
That I should be Little Miss Invisible,
The girl who isn't there!

PAIN

Ow, ow, ow, ow,
Tripping over and banging my nose.
Ow, ow, ow, ow,
Stubbing one of my ten tender toes.
Ow, ow, ow, ow,
Fall in the playground, bang my knee.
Ow, ow, ow, ow,
Scrape my shin climbing a tree.
Ow, ow, ow, ow,
Hit by a tennis ball in a painful place.
Ow, ow, ow, ow,
Scratch a spot on my face.
Ow, ow, ow, ow,
Whacked by my brother on my backside.
Ow, ow, ow, ow,
I can't help hurting myself, although I've tried.
Ow, ow, ow, ow,
Instead of chips I bite my tongue by mistake.
Ow, ow, ow, ow,
Why is it always me for goodness sake?
Ow, ow, ow, ow,
I asked my mum why I'm so prone

Ow, ow, ow, ow,

To living in a permanent accident zone.

Ow, ow, ow, ow,

She says I may be covered in plasters,

Ow, ow, ow, ow,

But there are even worse disasters.

Ow, ow, ow, ow,

She says the worst pain of all is the pain of the heart,

Ow, ow, ow, ow,

That's the body's most delicate part.

Ow, ow, ow, ow,

I tend to think she may be right,

Ow, ow, ow, ow,

Because my worst pain of all

Ow, ow, ow, ow,

Is when my parents have a fight.

55

STAY cLoSE To YOUR dREAMS

Stay close to your dreams.
Dive deeply into life's seas.
Don't just skim along the surface and stop,
Having collected all the filth that settles on top.

Dive, deep, deep, deep.
Find the hidden gems
That make life worth living.
Gems like hope and love and giving.
Treasure them,
Store them,
Safe and secure.
So that you can be sure
That whatever happens up on top,
You will still have your precious dreams close to you.

Never let your nightmares hold sway,
Don't let them see the light of day.
When, as they must, your dreams fade and vanish,
Dive again, dive again I say.

Dive as if your life depends on it.
For your dreams can hold you up
When nothing else can.

Dive. Dive. Dive.
Dream. Dream. Dream.

NO NAME

A boy came to school today Mum,
Who didn't seem to know his own name.
He seemed to look right through you
Though he did his work just the same.
But his work was huge scribbles,
Not neat words or careful sums.
My friend said she'd overheard something
From a cluster of whispering mums.
They said his mum used to call him 'You',
While his dad called him 'It'.
They said his whole house was a nasty dirty pit.
They said there had been a fight.
The police had been called round,
And in a filthy bedroom this boy had been found!

They thought he might be seven
Or maybe eight or even nine.
Mum, his face told a story of a different life than mine.
They asked him what his name was,
But he just stared blankly back.
They said that the courts have directed
His life down a different track.

He does seem very strange, Mum,
But I'd like to be his friend.
Do you think that story's true, Mum?
Or is it just pretend?

59

WAR GAMES

Rachel wouldn't tell Laura,
So Laura wouldn't tell me.
So I didn't know what to tell Rachel,
In fact I felt all at sea.

Rachel wanted to know what I knew.
What I knew was not much at all.
But she thought I knew more than I did know,
So she stormed off and sat by the wall.

So Laura went over to Rachel,
And then came over to me.
She said, "Rachel knows that you know,
So don't tell or there's trouble, do you see?"

Oh life would be far more fun
If friendships weren't such a muddle.
I don't like all this confusion,
I'd much rather just have a cuddle.
They're sharing secrets over by the wall
And probably calling me names.
Dear God, I just can't stand
These "I hate you!" "I love you!" war games!

THE ARGUMENT

Urgle, urgle, urgle, ooh.
That's all I want to say to you!
Slippy, sloppy, slappy, slee.
Don't you dare say that to me!
Fimble, famble, fumble, fo.
It's not nice to swear you know!
Hippy, hoppy, happy, hah.
This time you have gone too far!
Tittle, tattle, tottle, tain.
Arguing is such a pain.
Please can we be friends again?

ALWAYS

You're always calm.
I always get in a state.
You're always on time.
I'm always late.
You're always neat.
I'm always in a mess.
You always know the answers.
I always guess.
You're always at the heart of the action.
I always sit on the side.
You're always happy to be yourself.
I always try to hide.
You are my better self.
I'm the one who's shy.
Two personalities inside one body.
I always wonder why!

BLU-TAc BOY

I love to play with blu-tac.
It makes me feel secure,
And when it gets too dirty
I just go and get some more.

Sometimes people who don't know me
Think holding blu-tac isn't right,
But if they try to take it
There will be a fight.

For my blu-tac is my friend,
It will never answer back.
It gives me something to hold on to
When "the worries" attack.

To live without my blu-tac
Would be impossible to do,
For in this scary world
My blu-tac pulls me through!

iT'S A BoY THiNG

Score a great goal, dive in the dirt.
Brand new boots, number nine shirt.
It's just tough if you end up hurt.
Why? It's a boy thing!

Not really into working too hard,
Rather kick a ball around in the yard.
Too much writing gets a red card.
Why? It's a boy thing!

Show the girls we just don't care.
Leave them to whisper and comb their hair.
Though sometimes it's hard not to stare.
Why? It's a boy thing!

Not keen to tell you what we're feeling.
That's why we'd rather stare at the ceiling.
Not really into therapy and healing.
Why? It's a boy thing!

Jetting off to Hollywood, drive a fast car.
Girlfriends on our arms as we chat at the bar.
You just watch us. We're going far.
Why? It's a boy thing!

Lift off for life. We're getting ready.
Don't try to stop us, we've got to keep steady.
(But please, just let me keep my teddy.)
Why? It's a boy thing!

SUNRISE

(With thanks to Maya Angelou)

I'm up above the traffic lights
Far above the trees.
I'm high above the houses
I feel the cooling breeze.
I'm looking all around me
Over all the town.
I'm going to keep rising up
I'm never looking down.
I'm looking out across the fields
Far across the seas.
See me float, watch me rise
Travelling with ease.
I'm high above the clouds now,
Everything's bright blue.
I'm never stopping rising.
Are you rising too?
You think it's just a dream?
Right now it's coming true.
Watch me learn,
Hear me talk.
Can't you see it in my eyes?
Gravity can't keep me down
I am going to rise!

For Fitness and Football Fans

FOOTBALL DISASTER

I'm hipping, hopping
Bipping, bopping
Cross as cross can be.
I hurt my leg,
A big, strong lad came
Crunching in on me.
I wanted to be man of the match
But now I'm really sad.
I had to be subbed
Because I can't even walk
And now I'm hopping mad!

GUESS WHO?

Run, run, run,
As fast as you can.
You can't catch me,
I'm the Olympic man.

Everybody screaming:
"Go, go, go."
I've come to put on a show, show, show.
I've come from Jamaica.
I've got a huge grin.
And I'm going to use it when I win, win, win.

Run, run, run,
As fast as you can.
You can't catch me,
I'm the Olympic man.

THE CYCLE RACE

The wind is rushing across my face.
I'm riding in a cycle race.
Faster and faster my wheels spin.
The world's a blur. Can I win?
Heading for the finish, opposite the shop.
Got to keep going, my speed mustn't drop.
My heart's pumping madly,
It feels like it will burst.
We hurtle past the shop.
My position?
First!

cYcLES

Tricycle: 3 wheels, try it!
Bicycle: 2 wheels, buy it!
Unicycle: 1 wheel, you fall off it!

FiT cLUB

Push it, move it, work your body,
Get it on the go.
Bend it, shake it, spin your body,
No time to be slow.
Stretch it, pull it, twist your body,
Tummies, arms and thighs.
We're having fun at fit club.
Come on, let's exercise!

71

RUBBISH ROVERS

Get a spray can. Paint it up.
We have won the F.A. Cup.
F is for failures. A is for all.
We can't even kick a ball.
We're just a terrible waste of space.
Footballing flops, a real disgrace.
When a shot comes in, watch our keeper duck.
You can't call that just bad luck.
When our striker sees a gaping goal
He loses his footing and falls down a hole.
We're more "Wreck it like Wrexham"
Than "Bend it like Beckham"
But all the same we'll keep on trying.
We'd love to stop our fans from crying.
Maybe one day we might even win,
Then we'll throw our nightmare in the bin.
But until that day becomes more than a dream,
We remain the world's worst football team.

GAME OVER

[Throwing a scrunched-up piece of paper into a waste
paper basket]

He's going to shoot.
It's on its way, arcing perfectly towards the goal.
The crowd are going wild.
Oh, no. It's hit the post.
It's bounced out.
He's moving in for the rebound.
He must score this time.
Oh no, Mrs Smith, I mean the ref, has spotted him.
There's bound to be a card.
Will it be yellow or red?
It's only yellow.
What a relief.
He's back in his chair.
The ref's picked the ball up.
Oh no, the boy's still arguing.
It's going to be red this time.
It is. It's red.
He's off to the head's office.
He's gone.
The crowd sigh and return to their multiplication sums.
Game over.

73

For Fans of Animals and Nature

DOGGY DOGGY DO DO

Doggy doggy do do
All over the street

Doggy doggy do do
All over my feet

Doggy doggy do do
Should be in doggy loos

Doggy doggy do do
Ends up on my shoes

Doggy doggy do do
Messes up my floor

Dogs!
Do not do doggy doggy do do any more!

PANDAS

Pandas sit and chew bamboo.
They chew and chew and chew and chew.
All day long they chew bamboo.
Chewing bamboo's what pandas do.

THE GANG

They stare into your eyes.
They chew and chew.
They don't even care a bit about you.
They just love their grass and each other.
Protect your sister and your brother.
They roam the estate creating fear.
They are not popular around here.
Uprooting plants, frightening pensioners,
Blocking the roads, laughing at policemen,
Terrorising babies, injuring stray rabbits,
Invading gardens and knocking over swings.
They are deviant destroyers.
The wild sheep gang of Rawtenstall.
Baa!

PENGUIN DANCERS

Perfect penguin pals prance in the snow.
Boogie, woogie, woogie, everywhere they go.
Dancing all morning, then all afternoon.
Perfect penguin pals dance to every tune.

When they get worn out
And want a little rest,
They lay their penguin heads
In their little penguin nest.

Oh perfect penguin pals are
Ice dancers supreme.
In the Winter Olympics
They'd be the winning team.

SLEDGING AT CHRISTMAS

Sledging at Christmas was brilliant fun.
Storming down the hillside
On a sledge on my bum.
Bouncing off the fence
At the bottom of the hill,
Head still spinning, sledge finally still.
Covered in snow from head to toe,
Looking like an ice warrior
Emerging from a long-forgotten grave,
Frozen to the marrow,
But still feeling brave enough
To struggle back up for one more go.
You can keep your One Direction!
I'm in love with the snow.

 78

AFRICAN ANIMALS

Rhino, with your horn and your wrinkly skin,
Would you like some special cream
To keep your wrinkles in?

Hippo, you're so muddy.
Why don't you have a wash?
Just get yourself a shower
Then slosh, slosh, slosh.

Elephant, you are massive, huge, gigantic.
If you were to tread on me
You would send my mum quite frantic.

Lion, without doubt you are a fearsome cat,
With lots and lots of muscle but very little fat.

Leopard, sitting in your tree
With all your spots.
If I was brave and had a pencil
I could join up all your dots.

Giraffe, you are so very tall,
Though your legs are thin.
In a competition for the tallest animal you would win.

Eco School

Eco school, eco school.
This is an eco school.
Shout it out loud
Or whisper it quiet.
This is an eco school.
Why don't you try it?

Recycle your paper,
Recycle your cans,
Recycle your cycles,
Recycle your pans.

Save electricity,
Turn off the light.
Don't drop litter,
You know it's not right.

Build a pond,
Plant loads of seeds.
Tell the polluters
They're not meeting your needs.

Don't wait for the others,
Be eco friendly yourself.
Even if they leave the eco idea
Unused on a shelf.

We have a belief
And we know that it's right.
We'll keep doing our bit
Through the earth's dark night.

Eco school, eco school
This is an eco school.
Shout it out loud
Or whisper it quiet.
This is an eco school.
Why don't you try it?

81

SPLISH SPLASH

Splish splash
Splash splish
It's my lovely little fish.
Splat split
Split splat
It's been eaten by my cat.

 82

THE SLINK

The Slink is a beast with gingery hair.
He wears bright blue spotted underwear.
His tail is curly. His eyes are bright.
If you enter his cave he'll give you a fright.
Then he'll offer you tea and bake you a cake.
And sing you some songs which will keep you awake
Until well after midnight,
When he'll say with a wink:
"There's nothing in this world like the songs of a Slink."

DiARY OF A RAT LoVER

Saturday:
Went to the pet shop
Bought a rat.
He's black and hairy
And as big as our cat.

Sunday:
Scrubbed him clean,
Gave him a name:
'Super Mario'
After the computer game.

Monday:
Took Mario to school
For show and tell.
Calvin brought in his rat,
Snowy, as well.

Tuesday:
Put up a notice
In the school hall.
'Two rats lost' it said.
That was all.

84

Wednesday:
Got sent to the headteacher
With Calvin for fighting.
Calvin said Snowy ran off
Because Mario was biting.

Thursday:
Our classroom carpet
Has been eaten away.
We're not having
Another show-and-tell day.

Friday:
We found them curled up
Together on a mouse mat.
So is that the end of the tale
Of my escaping rat?

Not quite, because a few weeks later
I got a surprise.
In fact I could hardly believe my eyes.
Super Mario gave birth to six babies
Who were half black and half white.
Now we call her Super Maria,
Snowy's girlfriend.
And now we're family,
Calvin and I no longer fight.

THiS LiTTLE PiGGY

This little piggy's out shopping.
This little piggy needs the loo.
This little piggy can't find a toilet.
So doesn't know what to do.

This little piggy is desperate,
So dashes home all alone.
Poor little piggy is too late.
He goes: 'wee wee wee' all the way home.

ANTEATERS

Anteaters don't eat bubble gum.
It's too chewy.
Anteaters don't eat cows.
They're too mooey.
Anteaters don't eat glue.
It's too gluey.
Anteaters don't eat custard.
It's too gooey.
Anteaters don't eat stew.
It's too stewey.
Anteaters don't eat food that's too
Chewy, mooey, gluey, gooey or stewey.
Anteaters only eat ants!

87

THE NORTH WIND BLOWS

Up and up the red balloon goes,
Escaping from home as the north wind blows.
Soon it's a pinprick in the sky,
Speeding away, see it fly.

Up and up, watch it swirl and sway.
The red balloon's racing, no time to stay.
Through the Midlands, past London and on.
Over the Channel, England's gone.

The red balloon leaps, plays and dances.
Down through France it cavorts and prances.
Hurtling yet faster, on towards Spain,
Over the mountains and on again.

The weather in Africa is burning hot.
Above the Sahara the balloon's a red spot.
The camel herders sniff the air,
Not knowing our balloon's up there.

They're waiting for the coming rain,
To make the desert bloom again.
As the wind rises, our balloon's rising too,
As the warm air currents push on through.

The drought breaks, the lightning flashes.
The rain pours, the thunder crashes.
Our tiny balloon bursts and dies.
Its journey is over. The desert cries.

FUZZY BUZZY

Fuzzy Buzzy bumble bee
Buzzed around so joyfully,
Then fell into a cup of tea.
Poor Fuzzy Buzzy.

Fuzzy Buzzy tried to swim.
Swimming was too hard for him.
Things were really looking grim.
Poor Fuzzy Buzzy.

Fuzzy Buzzy soaking wet,
Tiny girl said, "He's my pet.
He will be my best pet yet."
Poor Fuzzy Buzzy.

Fuzzy Buzzy in a jar.
Couldn't fly very far,
Wished that he could see his ma.
Poor Fuzzy Buzzy.

Fuzzy Buzzy free at last,
Girl got bored, chucked him fast,
Hopes his bad luck's in the past.
Poor Fuzzy Buzzy.

Fuzzy Buzzy bumble bee
Buzzed around so joyfully.
Please keep away from cups of tea.
Good luck, Fuzzy Buzzy.

A WINTER VISITOR

Jack Frost seemed to be lost,
Then one day he was found.
He left his cold, white cloak
Covering the ground.

"Where have you been?"
The children said.
"You've been gone so long,
We feared you were dead."

"Oh no," replied Jack,
"I cannot die.
While the earth has life,
Then so shall I."

"Then where have you been?"
The children said.
"To be away so long
That we feared you were dead."

"Ah," replied Jack.
"The place that I go,
Is the northern land
Of ice and snow."

"I dine there every night
With the polar bears,
On freezing fish soup
And Arctic hares."

"But we miss you so,"
The children said.
"Please don't dash away,
Stay longer instead."

But not one promise
Would Jack Frost give.
He grinned as he declared,
"I live as I live."

By the very next day
He was nowhere to be seen.
Jack Frost had gone again
And the world was green.

93

For Fans of Maths and Tongue Twisters

cALLUM cOX

Callum Cox has special socks
Which he locks
In a strong socks box.
Callum Cox's socks box has three locks
And two alarm clocks.
One clock rings and rocks
If anyone
Except Callum Cox
Knocks his socks box.
Callum Cox's socks box
Is like Fort Knox.
So unless you want the shock of all shocks,
Do not knock Callum Cox's socks box.

PLAYTIME PROBLEMS

Billy bit Ben
Because Ben bit Billy.
Ben said he bit Billy
Because Billy was a bit silly.
Billy bit Ben back
So Ben gave Billy a bit of a whack.
If Billy and Ben become
Best friends again tomorrow,
Both Billy and Ben might be okay,
But Miss Brown says neither Billy nor Ben
Will be going out to play.

95

TAKE AWAYS

If they took away take aways
They'd be taking away subtraction.
Take aways are some people's
Favourite maths attraction.
But if they took away take aways
You'd hear this cry from many others:
"Hurray. They've taken away take aways.
Let's run and tell our mothers."
But they'll never take away take aways
So there's no need to cheer or to worry.
If you do want to take away a take away
Get down to your local take away
And take away a curry!

FIVE HUNGRY FLIES

Five hungry flies
Sucking jam from the floor
One stuck to a strawberry
So that left four.

Four hungry flies
Desperate for their tea
One was pounced on by the cat
So that left three.

Three hungry flies
Feasting on Mum's stew
One fell in and drowned
So that left two.

Two hungry flies
Munching on a currant bun
One fell off and crushed a wing
So that left one.

One not-so-hungry fly
Feeling full of currant bun
Flew out through the window
And that left none.

i don't know

I don't know what I don't know.
How can I?
I don't know it.
I only know what I do know.
There's no way I can know what I don't know.
I'll never know what I don't know.
Until I know it.
Then it won't be what I don't know.
It will be what I do know.
Is that so?
Do you know?

TEN TIRED TOMATOES

Ten tired tomatoes sleeping on a plate,
Two woke up and left, then there were eight.

Eight juicy tomatoes performing circus tricks,
Two fell off the high wire and then there were six.

Six strange tomatoes dancing round an apple core,
Two fell over, far too dizzy, then there were four.

Four furry tomatoes, far too mouldy to chew,
Two were thrown in the compost, then there were two.

Two terrified tomatoes, knowing it's their turn now,
Squish, squish, squish,
Ow, ow, ow.

DOUBLING

Me and you
That makes 2
2 more
That makes 4
Doubling is great
Double 4 is 8
Are you getting what I mean?
Double 8 is 16
Is it becoming hard for you?
Double 16 is 32
Let's keep going, let's do more
Double 32 is 64

Now for the hundreds, let's not wait
Double 64 is 128
What's next in our mathematical mix?
Double 128 is 256
Let's keep doubling, let's dig and delve
Double 256 is 512
Now for the thousands, what's in store?
Double 512 is 1024
One final step to prove doubling's great
Double 1024 is 2048
We could go on doubling forever and ever.
There's no end to numbers, never, never.
But then this poem would go on forever too.
So if you want to carry on doubling.
From now on it's up to you.

For Body Fans

Got To Go

Got to go, got to go
I just can't wait.
Got to go, got to go
It's nearly too late.
Got to go, got to go
My bladder is talking.
Got to go, got to go
I'm running not walking.
Got to go, got to go
There's someone on the loo.
Got to go, got to go
What can I do?
Got to go, got to go
I've got to go now!
Got to go, got to go
I can't wait, ow!
Got to go, got to go
It's my turn at last.
Ahh
That's better,
The crisis is past!

LiPS

Lips are for pouting,
For spreading wide when you're shouting.
Lips are for licking,
For painting if you're lip-sticking!

Lips are for silence breaking,
For funny noise making.
Lips are your mouth's security check,
Sensitive to the tiniest speck.

Now let's see,
What's still missing?

Oh yes,
Lips are for kissing!

THE WOMB

I wish I could remember the womb,
My comfy, cosy growing-up room.
The constant thump of Mum's heart,
My first days, my life's start.

It must have been dark in there
And lonely with no twin to share.
Just an umbilical cord connecting me
To an outside world that I couldn't see.

But can you feel lonely inside another?
For I was literally part of my mother.
It took scissors or the knife
To cut the cord linking me to her life.

No wonder our bond is so strong,
We were together for so long.
Mum walked around with me inside,
No separation: nowhere to hide.

 104

Then after nine months: expulsion.
Into the world propulsion.
Mum's lung-bursting cries,
"Isn't he sweet!" sighs.

I wish I could remember the womb.
My comfy, cosy growing-up room.
All of a sudden I was out and free.
My very own person: Me!

NOSE BLEED

Blood on the table,
Blood on the floor.
Blood everywhere, watch it pour.
Out of my nose,
Gushing like a tap.
I wish I could turn it off,
Just like that.
But it's rushing and gushing,
On and on it goes.
Like a rolling red stream,
Whose source is my nose.
My world has changed,
Its colour is red.
A whole sea of blood,
From out of my head.

EYEBROWS

Up and down,
Up and down,
Up and down they go.
Move them fast, move them slow.
Up and down they go.
Made of hair, dark or fair.
Shave them off
They won't be there.
Then up and down,
Up and down,
Up and down
They won't go.
No, no, no.

LEGS

Running, hopping, jumping legs,
Dancing, moving, grooving legs.
Leaping high towards the sky.
From the ankle to the thigh.
Long, lovely, loose limb.
Can be big, can be thin.
Full of muscle, full of fat,
Full of blood and stuff like that.
Legs, legs, legs, legs, legs!

BRIAN THE BRAIN

My brain is called Brian.
He's an anagram.
Brian is my main man.

Swap the a for an i,
Then, my oh my,
Brain becomes Brian.
That's why Brian is the name of my brain.

He's always cooking up ideas.
He's also the source of my hopes and my fears.
Brian is always working.
His motto is: "No shirking!"

Even at night when I'm fast asleep,
He's active in my dreams to reveal the secrets I keep.
He is amazing is Brian my brain.
Without him I think I'd go quite insane.

EARDRUMS

Eardrums resonate,
Vibrate, amplify
Sound all around.
So even the tiniest lost sound
Ends up found.
All thanks to an eardrum.
Ti tum, ti tum, ti tum.

THE HEART

As full of blood as a blood bank.
As ready to burst as a water bomb.
As important as life itself.
Your heart is a miracle of
Imagination and design.
I'm so glad that you've got yours
And I've got mine.
But hearts can break.
They can ache.
They can bleed.
They can lead you into
Heartbreak and heartache.
But there is no alternative.
For we must love!

FOR FINAL THOUGHTS FANS

LONG LIVE THE BLOB

It's large. It's round.
It blobs all around.
It's fab. It's fun.
It helps everyone.
It will pick you up if you fall,
And hear your voice when you call.
It will always try to understand.
It's always keen to lend a hand.
It will dry your tears when you sob.
It's my hero.
It's the blob.

It's very keen on education
For every child in every nation.
It knows that as we love and learn
We bless others in our turn.
The blob's belief is that our teachers
Are the world's most wondrous creatures.

Not everyone is the blob's fan.
But I think the blob's the man.
I won't listen to the moaning mob.
For my hero is the blob!

In Another's Chair

I'm sitting in another's chair.
Not my own.
I'm in another's chair.

Many have sacrificed a lot
So that I can have all that I've got.
I've had countless ancestors
Since the dawn of time,
Living their lives
So I can live mine.
I'm in another's chair.
I need to remember,
I'm lucky to be there!

HOME FOR GOOD

The human heart wasn't made to be broken.
Every person needs to hear these words spoken:
"You are loved not for what you do
But for who you are."
It's that voice which can carry us far,
Away from the loneliness,
Into a land called home,
Where we can live and love
And never be alone.

THE WEAVER

Weaving life together is a stretch.
Sometimes I feel I'm on the wrong side of the tapestry.
Loose threads tangle everywhere.
I'm a puppet dangling helplessly.

Sometimes though I glimpse the front of the tapestry
Where there's beauty, cohesion and
Splashes of radiant colour.
Then I praise the weaver who brings
Order out of chaos and
Beauty out of pain.
It's then I find the strength to rise and stretch again.

THE BATTLE

To communicate thought
Is a battle often fought
But not often won.
I want to be one who wins that war
For what else is a poet for!

MY PRAYER

As a visiting poet in your school,
May I listen as much as I talk.
May I recall that before I could run I had to walk.
May I see each child as just as important as every other.
May I remember that everyone here is my sister or brother.
May I provide an opportunity for every soul to sing.
May I reflect something of the perfect love that you bring.
May I be fair and kind to everyone.
And may I bring to this place
Just a little bit of fun.

BE

Be kind, be honest, be fair.
Beware of a grizzly bear.
Be short, be tall, be long.
Be right, be left, be wrong.
Be good, be safe, behave.
Be hairy or get a shave.
Bee buzzes all around.
Be rich if you've got a pound.
B comes just after A.
Be careful what you say.
Be a crazy beeping poet just like me or
Be whatever you want to be!